Essential Expressions of

The Vital Force

Jacqueline A. Smith S.C.Hom(Dist.)T.Q.F.E. MLitt.

CLC Publications

British Library Cataloguing-in-Publication Data
A catalogue record for this book is available on request from the British Library
ISBN 9781838532864

Contents

Introduction

This book begins where I began. To heal is to learn. When my healing began it was initiated at all levels. Through many healing crises learning has prevailed. Reading psychology as a teenager of fifteen years, quickly had me doubting my upbringing. Specifically, in the first instance, how my dysfunctional family interacted with each other. Doubting what I had come, with catholic conditioning, to believe was the norm but the story no longer seemed plausible. Life didn't have to be that way!

Now there were choices I hadn't known existed. The realisation made me an insufferable know-it-all for a time. Someone who criticised indiscriminately and demanded change in those around me. Ah! You say, but of course the change has to come from within, everyone knows that! Well, everyone thinks they do and on an intellectual level maybe they do, but that on its own isn't enough to effect real change.

Jung's archetypes and the animus concept initially helped me acknowledge the richness of multidimensional being that I carried within. By watching my dreams and listening to the hidden story of my fears and resultant postures, I slowly began to edge away from what had been prescribed for my life so far.

The help of friends outside my familiar circle supported the shift, but then I just seemed to take on their thoughts and attitudes. Soon it was other thought systems, other alternatives to my childhood conditioning. Buddhism became my new point of reference via Carl Jung's intro in 'The Secret of the Golden Flower' That became a long relationship of thirty-some years with its core of mind training as my guide to the skills of focus, insight and awareness with the balance in the cultivation of compassion and wisdom.

Motherhood came at the same time as my practice of meditation and the struggle to evolve took on another dimension; gave me more elements to include; to embrace in my life practice. The Four Noble Truths and the Noble Eightfold Path of Buddhist scripture became my path in life. Having children brought up, for me, the conflicts between natural living choices in food and healthcare and those conventionally accepted. I favoured the natural and the origins of those four noble truths: *the truth of suffering, the truth of the cause of suffering, the truth of the end of suffering, and the truth of the path that leads to the end of suffering,* being from an ancient approach to healing fundamental to my daily practice, led me onto a centuries-old healing system that was from my own side of the world.

This born-in-the-past Art and Science of homeopathy is still being nurtured for the future despite the onslaught of the pharmaceutical industry. This complete system of medicine is still curing numberless people around the world and could help many millions more if profit, rather than quality of life, was not the prevalent harmful driving force in our 21st century world.

This book is about how homeopathy can and does help. How its philosophy is fundamental to the underlying **M**ultiple **S**trands of life and their expression.

I will aim to outline a process using background research, visual diagrams and images that will help homeopaths, students and others to utilise an elemental circle that will enhance their understanding of the relationships between Acute and Chronic remedies, using specific polychrest remedy pictures (or vibrational patterns).

In learning this process, it will result in

+ Understanding the qualities and related properties of the elements enabling one to perceive the ***Essence*** of any particular *vibrational pattern*

- Understanding the flow (or rate of energy) of a *vibrational pattern,* enabling recognition of its similarities or differences to other remedies
- Understanding the nature and type of expression manifesting at the four levels of disease, enabling recognition of the type of treatment (i.e. Acute, Episodic, Acute of the Chronic or Chronic) and subsequently the remedy required.

i) Helping to achieve some holistic awareness of the interaction and inter relationship between the elemental energies and all other *vibrational patterns.*

The Vital Force

What is the meaning of "vital force theory" in e.g. organic chemistry?

According to vital force theory, organic compounds must have their origin in living organisms and could never be synthesized from inorganic material. This theory is known as the vital force theory.

Vital Force Theory

Jacob Berzelius, (20 August 1779 – 7 August 1848) was a Swedish chemist. Berzelius is considered, along with Robert Boyle, John Dalton, and Antoine Lavoisier, to be one of the founders of modern chemistry. Berzelius became a member of the Royal Swedish Academy of Sciences in 1808 and gave this theory in 1809. According to this theory, the organic living compounds are not formed from inorganic compounds but a vital force. This vital force or spiritual force is called by some, God. Though the Vital Force Theory was rejected in 1823 by mainstream and reductionist minds when Friedrich Wöhler synthesized the first organic compound urea from an inorganic compound, Ammonium cyanate; it has never been rejected beyond the physical by those who recognise alternative approaches to science.

Berzelius defined this theory in 1815, setting down three principles with it:

1. Organic compounds cannot be made in the laboratory from inorganic compounds.

2. The synthesis of organic compounds requires a vital force.

3. Only living organisms (God-given) contain this vital force.

At this time, when homeopathy first evolved in the 18th century, the Vital Force was a more readily accepted concept as being a primal force determining a person's state of health. Dr. Samuel Hahnemann (1755-1843) in his Organon of Homeopathic Medicine described it as a dynamic, immaterial, spirit-like force that embodies the **essence** of life and all of its metabolic and functional activities. The Vital Force is a very important organizing force of life that directs your evolution towards reaching your full potential.

The Vital Force is a purely energetic and immaterial entity. It has recognizable characteristics that tell you of its presence but it cannot be localized within the physical body except using e.g. the schema of Chinese meridians or the Chakras.

The dynamic nature of the Vital Force allows it to respond in a holistic way instantaneously to all factors influencing a person. All your parts and all functions are equally assessed and influenced by the Vital Force. Though the Vital Force is immaterial, its actions are expressed and observable in an individual both as a whole and in all of their individual parts. These represent the signs and symptoms available to practitioners in guiding their assessment and treatment. The homeopathic physician makes a different assessment of signs and symptoms than might be made in allopathic medicine due to the awareness of the Vital Force.

Examples of digestion and breathing are used to demonstrate the presence, the capabilities, and the functioning of the Vital Force. These examples demonstrate the Vital Force's place in the hierarchy of influences that determine both our health and our life experience. From this perspective it can be postulated that homeostasis could be regarded as a function of the Vital Force. These examples serve to contrast the Vital Force with the conscious mind. Both systems influence how we think, how we act, and the consequences these thoughts and actions have on our physical body.

A key concept is that the Vital Force will only create a response to what you experience in life that is ideal for your state of health, your health history, your health potential and your life challenges. The Vital Force maintains balance in your health. The Vital Force prioritises your response to stress both when life's stresses do not exceed your strength and also when a challenge exceeds your capabilities or experience by creating the perfect symptoms of a disease state.

In brief the vital force is:

- Life force, vital energy, dynamis.
- The vital principle or animating force within living beings: breath, divine spark, élan vital, psyche, soul, spirit, vitality.
- The VF is unique in each and every individual organism
- The VF acts on the trinity of: Mind, Body and Spirit
- In health the VF is strong and balanced
- In disease the VF is disturbed and out of balance
- 'The invisible spirit-like vital force, when deranged, produces symptoms that are outwardly recognisable. This means symptoms are an outward expression of the inner turmoil' (Organon §15)

The Vital Force and Disease

When a plant or animal is diseased, or when we become unwell, we often look to the symptoms as the cause of the problem. In reality, symptoms are only secondary changes – products of a deeper disturbance.

Apart from injury, the symptoms of disease and ill-health can only occur when there has been a disruption to the energetic Vital Force. This disruption can occur from psychic (mental rather than physical) shocks such as deep grief, prolonged anxiety, terror, disappointment, or even extreme joy. Physical shocks may come from infectious diseases, exposure to the elements, trauma, malnutrition, extreme exertion, and so on.

The Vital Force, when disrupted energetically by one of these events (or Exciting Causes), strives to regain balance and preserve life. In the course of this effort, it produces signs and symptoms. These symptoms are not the disturbance but only by-products of the attempt to heal. In the case of acute problems such as the flu, gastroenteritis, and headaches, the Vital Force is usually successful: we recover and symptoms subside.

Sometimes it is unable to regain balance, though, and the imbalance leads to death. On other occasions the acute problem gradually morphs into a chronic disease. Chronic disease may arise from unresolved acute problems, or directly from the mental, emotional and physical events that are part of life.

Chronic diseases are too numerous to list but include problems such as lung complaints, digestive problems, skin disorders and various types of arthritis. Unlike acute problems they do not go away but gradually lead to worsening health as the person ages. Unless the end of life comes from a sudden acute event, most people die from the long-term damage caused by their chronic disease or diseases.

While the imbalance created by acute disease can be overcome by the Vital Force, the imbalance created by a chronic disease cannot - the Vital Force can only contain and limit it. The cost of engaging in a long-term attempt to preserve life is the production of long-term symptoms.

Once again, the symptoms are not the true disease - just the by-product of this deeper energetic process. They do, however, give us important information on how to help the Vital Force correct and restore equilibrium so that the sufferer can be fully returned to a state of health.

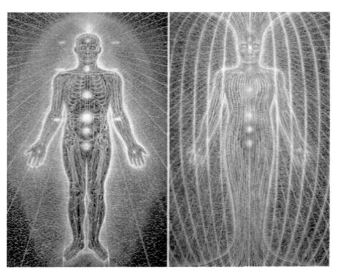

Alex Grey   Psychic Energy System   Spiritual Energy System

The Four Laws of Cure and other Principles.

Throughout this book there will be discussion of energetic principles from one perspective or another. The similarities and notes of resonance will become apparent. We are exploring the energy of life aka the Vital Force, Chi, Prana, Ki etc. and then energies of love and joy bubble up when healing occurs and life is transformed.

This is how we know healing has taken place. The learning is seen when new ways of being are discovered and integrated with acceptance of who we are, as we are.

Evolution is a key theme, i.e. that of emerging out of what has been before; health and wholeness out of dis-ease. We will begin by exploring the principles of homeopathy through another universal energetic medium - Music.

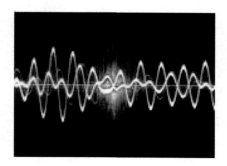

The Music of Homeopathy-Symphony No.1

PRELUDE

"Music is the real universal speech of humankind." **C.F. Weber.**

This is an exploration of Homoeopathy using the language of music as a metaphor, with a symphonic structure in sonata form (i.e., four parts). As a two-hundred-year old system of medicine, which is based on consideration of the effects of disturbances to the subtle inner nature of human beings, and which existed before, for example, the formulation of theories or acceptance of the existence of anything like an Electro-Dynamic Human Energy Field or Kirlian photography, **HOMOEOPATHY** has had to borrow many musical terms to describe both diseased states and their treatment.

Many of these terms are still also akin to those in use to describe the movement and qualities of energy. Both analogies are appropriate. The energy patterns of both the human organism i.e. instrument (particularly, the voice in the production of sounds) in disease states and the patterns of remedy pictures are referred to time and again, as having the utmost importance in the literature of Homoeopathy. E.g. **a Remedy Picture must resonate with the Total Symptom Picture of an individual being treated homoeopathically.** The effect of resolving a disturbance in this way would be described as using counter-poise in terms of musical composition i.e., a force or influence that balances or equally counteracts another, resulting in a state of equilibrium.

OVERTURE (1st Movement)

*"When a human falls ill it is at first only this self-sustaining spirit-like vital force everywhere present in the organism which is **untuned** by the dynamic influence of the…. disease agent."* Samuel Hahnemann (1755-1843) Para 11. The Organon of Medicine 6th Edition, "A New Translation. Pub. Victor Gollanz Ltd. 1989)

*"It is only the pathologically **untuned** vital force that causes diseases. These…manifestations accessible to our senses express all the internal changes, i.e., the whole pathological disturbance of the dynamis: they reveal the whole disease.* "(S.H. para.12, Organon)

Since Homoeopathy was founded as a system of medicine in the late 17th century by Samuel Hahnemann, there has been an increasing upheaval in the way humans choose to regard their ails and ills.

This essay that you now read, itself attests to the resurgence of esteem for the 'connections' between body, mind and emotions. The dissonance that many of us have or will experience at some time in our lives is now being viewed in many quarters with an apparently 'new' perspective. It appears there has been a paradigm shift.

INTERLUDE

SONG OF SEPIA

Sepia sings as she washes the clothes,
Sings and laments over worries and woes.
"What is this burden I carry around,
SAG on the inside, weighing me down?"

Sepia chants in an apathetic drone,
Wife, home and children mean little,
It's clear from his tone.
Indifferent, he wails, Leave me alone!

So, if you happen to hear their irritable dirge,

Let compassion arouse, get them out of the house!
So much better are they, if they do something active,
Then they are seen at their most attractive!

2nd MOVEMENT (Slow & Extended)

*'In the state of health the spirit-like vital force (dynamis) animating the material human organism reigns in supreme sovereignty. It maintains the sensations and activities of all the parts of the living organism in a **harmony** that obliges wonderment. The reasoning spirit who inhabits the organism can thus freely use this healthy living **instrument** to reach the highest purposes of human existence.'*
(S.H Para.9. The Organon of Medicine.)

When working with fellow patients' Vital Force to aid their healing, we learn to work with the symbolic substance of life which often speaks in metaphors and similes, i.e., people often begin to describe their varied sensations and feelings with "It's as if…." Or "It's like…"

We become watchers of the shifting images and hopefully the **liet motiv**, which illustrates the essence of their suffering. We listen to and trust in these inner patterns that unfold, so that it is possible to help fellow patients participate and co-operate with the possible transformation that can occur during the process of cure.

To understand and recognize the nature of this energy we need to develop a new archetype; a new way of relating to and experiencing both our own and the patients' inherent wholeness. This archetype is not a form or structure but a sacred space within, where we are able to reconnect with our own **essential** nature and therefore with that of others requesting help to heal themselves.

The nature of this space is defined more by its qualities of connection and similarity rather than by boundaries and limitations. It can allow us to be our own true self and to recognize the individuality of others. Within such a space it is possible to feel the sacred wholeness of all life and at the same time appreciate the profound uniqueness of each facet of creation; of each perfect note. However, this newly emerging archetype is not yet present when we first encounter both our own process of healing or those who seek homoeopathic treatment. Instead, we are confronted by the decaying forms and distorted manifestations of consciousness. Old patterns and outmoded rhythms must be let go; must die for the new to be born, but it is mainly these **discordant melodies** that are perceived. They are still in the forefront of our consciousness whether we are aware of them or not and will express themselves through the physical form as disease states which we are conditioned to notice and value.

'When not in freedom the individual says, "I feel..." It is this disturbance of an invisible character which comes from cause, and appears by changes in the activities of the body, changes in sensations, changes in functions.... No feeling a human can have is without purpose, as there is nothing in the universe without its use.' **(Dr. J.T. Kent, "Lectures on Homoeopathic Philosophy." Pg.79. B. Jain Publishers)**

As healers and wayfarers on the path of healing and transformation we learn to welcome what we do not yet know – that which is coming from beyond into consciousness; a new aria, an enlivening euphony. The new will always be threatening to those of us attached to the old ways, to the forms created in the past. Yet amidst the structures we have created and evolved from the past, the present is dynamically alive, not as a problem to be solved but as life giving of itself. It is a seed that must be sown with the appropriate energy to bring us into consciousness of the nature of our disease, of the quality and form, which initially must be identified and then urged to move on. When we remain in identification with outmoded rhythms and forms we can become isolated because forms are defined by their separateness. In space there is flow; and in its movement the music of life is hidden. Rhythm is more than a mere harmonizing influence; it is the vehicle for higher or subtler forms of experience.

Human consciousness is carried on rhythms of heart-beat, breathing, sleeping and waking, night-day, winter-summer, and life and death itself. In Homoeopathic treatment the practitioner can use **the Minimum Dose** of a dynamically resonant **Single Remedy** to help create space by matching **the essence** of the chosen remedy picture to **the essence** of the distorted pattern manifesting in the patient. Otherwise, imprisoned in the forms we have created, life ceases to flow from the source, disease results and problems abound. When those who come to seek solutions appear, what their learning and healing process encompasses is to recognize the need to open themselves so that life can flow freely. Healers of all

18

kinds cannot exempt themselves, it is the learning we all need. It is life flowing from and to its source that will heal the earth, just as in humans the **Vital Force** is the prime agent in any personal healing.

3rd MOVEMENT (Minuet – Regular rhythm)

*"Outer malefic agents that harm the healthy organism and disturb the **harmonious rhythm of life** can reach and effect the spirit-like dynamis only in a way that is also dynamic and spirit-like. The physician can remove these pathological **untunements** (dis-eases) only by acting on our spirit-like vital force with medicines having equally spirit-like dynamic effects that are perceived by the nervous sensitivity everywhere present in the organism.*

So it is only by dynamic action upon the vital principle that remedies can restore health and the harmony of life after perceptible changes in health (the totality of symptoms) have revealed the disease to the carefully observing and inquiring physician fully enough to be cured." S.H. Para.16. The Organon of Medicine

In the Overture, we mentioned briefly that Homoeopathy is based on **The Law of Similars**. This in fact states '**Let likes be cured by likes'** and this is the point of resonance that is required to treat the aforementioned **Totality of Symptoms**. But this is not the only reason why homoeopathic treatment can be so swift-acting, so deeply affecting or so subtle and direct in its action. Another hugely important factor is that homoeopathic remedies are **potentised** or dynamised. This brings us closer to the counter-point where the language of music and descriptions of energy and its qualities meet. Samuel Hahnemann's second outstanding contribution to medicine was made when he devised the technique of **potentisation**. At first he tried to dilute substances chosen by the **Law of Similars** to treat patients and he immediately found this reduced toxic effects of the substances, but it also appeared to reduce the therapeutic effects in proportion to the amount of dilution. Whether through his background in chemistry and/or inspiration from some other source, Hahnemann hit upon the idea of adding kinetic energy (or rhythmic vibration) to the **diluted** substances by shaking or '**succussion**'. The ground-breaking effect he observed was that the combination of serial dilution and succussion brought a greater therapeutic effect whilst still extinguishing the toxic effects of the substances.

The result was the development of an ingenious but simple technique of extracting the therapeutic energy of a substance without altering its pattern, which could therefore still be administered according to the basic resonance principle of the **Law of Similars**, but now with the enhanced effects of an increased intensity of pitch in the electro-dynamic field of the therapeutic agent. The liberated energy originally contained within the crude substance is now abler to interact with the dynamic plane of the organism and produce a lasting cure of the total organism.

*"**Aggravation'** is...used in homoeopathic parlance to describe those conditions in which, under the action of a deeply acting homoeopathic medicine (or from other causes), latent disease becomes active and expresses itself in the return of the old symptoms...In such cases it represents the reaction of the organism to the stimulus of a well selected medicine, and is generally curative in its nature."* Stewart Close Pg.152 The Genius of Homoeopathy; B. Jain Publishers

The nature and purpose of the Homoeopathic aggravation has caused much, at times, controversial debate over the years both in the Homoeopathic profession, amongst patients undergoing treatment and in medical circles. It represents the greatest departure from other therapeutic systems because its place in homoeopathy heralds an exceptional view of the process of cure, i.e. homoeopathy does not consider the simple disappearance or removal of symptoms to mean that someone has been cured of their disease. As indicated in the above quotation, the prescription of a deeply resonant Single Remedy given at any one time, which produces an aggravation, shows the homoeopath, that the vital force of the patient has recognized its similimum. It is therefore desirable that the organism responds by attempting to throw off symptoms which have previously been suppressed by defensive postures, allopathic drugs or by will power.

"To be completely free, an organism must be fully expressive and creative in the context of its immediate reality. When its expression is inhibited, suppressed, rendered secret, or obstructed, then we have an ill individual." **Prof. George Vithoulkas Pg. 228 "The Science of Homoeopathy." B. Jain Pub.**

20

Again, in the quotation at the start of our finale, it is stated that the **aggravation** is 'generally curative'. This is not the case when repeated doses of a remedy are given without waiting to assess the response of the vital force, (e.g., remedies that are sold in health shops often have instructions that they should be taken three times daily for a month!) What is likely to happen in these cases is that, whether the remedy is apparently the 'correct' one or not, the person can begin to manifest symptoms that they did not previously have; their original symptoms may worsen and remain so or they may be suppressed to a greater degree than with, for example, antibiotics. If the person begins to exhibit symptoms of the remedy, not an aggravation of their original complaint, which may be suppressed by 'overdosing' of the chosen remedy, this is what is known as a **'proving'**. Though 'provings' have great value in controlled Human Pathogenetic Testing to discover the effects of substances that are the source of remedies.

It is a myth that Homoeopathic remedies are always safe. They are only so when used properly and their effects monitored by someone who is trained, at least to some degree, to be able to differentiate whether the process of cure has been initiated or not. Professional homoeopaths are trained to assess the action of remedies by using the clearly stipulated **Four Laws of Cure**, which were formulated by Constantine Hering (1800-1880).

In general, and briefly, they are as follows:

- **Symptoms move from the innermost (vital) organs of the body to the outer organs.**
- **Cure takes place from above downwards.**
- **Symptoms move from within, outwards.**
- **Symptoms clear in reverse order of appearance.**

Some diagrams of remedy pictures as Elemental Circles and deepening pathology will be provided to illustrate levels of health and disease as **the vital force** moves into the healing process.

Obviously, the process of cure for each person is as individual as they are, but it takes some considerable understanding of the disease process from a homoeopathic perspective in order to accurately assess the dynamics of each case. After a thorough training in homoeopathic theory and clinical practice, there is no greater teacher than experience in accumulating the skills necessary to tune the ear to hear the individual **melody**, thereby being able to choose the **Keynote** symptoms expressing the **liet motiv** leading to the **Simillimum**, and to further discern a curative response after applying the **Single Remedy** in the **Minimum Dose**.

COUNTER-POINT

"Emotions of any kind are produced by melody and rhythm; therefore, by music a human becomes accustomed to feeling the right emotions; music has thus the power to form character, and the various kinds of music based on the various modes, may be distinguished by their effects on character – e.g., working in the direction of melancholy, ... one encouraging abandonment, another self-control, another enthusiasm and so on through the series." **ARISTOTLE**

"It has long been recognised that music is a universal means of communication. It has been called a non-verbal language. What has yet to be more fully realised is the range of expression that is possible in this 'language'. The variety of human experience that can be communicated through music is highly diversified and virtually unlimited."

C. Robbins & Dr. P. Nordoff in "Music Therapy; A New Anthology" (New Knowledge Books)

Healing happens...

From above downwards
From within outwards

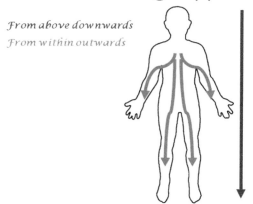

Healing happens...

From a more important organ to a less important one

In reverse order of their coming

Ex) Heart to spleen

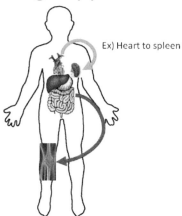

Image credits: Sarah Walder

The Four Elements

Introduction

In order to introduce the four elements as a schema which can be used to interpret the energies inherent in remedies and patterns of energy which present themselves through the *symptom picture* of a patient, it is necessary to go back to some of the earliest history of medicine in the western world and ascertain how and by whom they have been considered as formative forces.

The first individual in the western hemisphere, (the eastern hemisphere has a longer history), who is considered to have believed the elements to be a fundamental influence on our expression, was a Greek philosopher and statesman by the name of EMPEDOCLES (490-430BC).

He is described as "...at once a believer in Orphic mysteries and a scientific thinker." He held that there are four ultimate and unchangeable elements, four primal divinities; of which all structures in the world are made: FIRE, AIR, WATER, and EARTH.

According to Empedocles, these four roots of all things are eternally brought into union and eternally parted by two active corporeal forces; love and strife.

These two forces can be seen working amongst humankind, but which really pervade the whole world. In Empedocles' view nothing new comes or can come into being; the only change that can occur is a change in the juxtaposition of element with element.

What is very interesting about the elemental philosophy of the world propounded by Empedocles is that it would appear as a very early forerunner of what eventually became the homoeopathic Law of Similars. This is often mainly attributed to Hippocrates (460-357BC) among others; but let us have a closer look at Empedocles' Doctrine.

He further propounded that since humans, animals, and plants are composed of the same elements in different proportion, they have an identity of nature.

They all have sense and understanding, and mind in humanity always being dependent upon the body. Knowledge is explained by the principle that several elements in things are perceived by the corresponding elements in us. i.e. **'LIKE IS KNOWN BY LIKE."**

The organs of sense are said to be specially adapted to receive the effluxes from bodies around us and in this way arises perception which is not merely passive.

In addition, there was also the doctrine that the Divinity (and Vital Force?) passes from element to element and may have been used as a spiritual way of teaching that the principles (i.e., the elemental forces) underlie every phase of development from inorganic nature to humankind.

Even more fascinating is that at the top of the scale of development Empedocles puts the *Prophet* and the *physician*; those who have best learned the secret of life. They are next to the divine!

It is said that it is the business of the *philosopher* to lay bare the fundamental difference of elements and to display the identity between what seem to be unconnected parts of the universe.

The elements are also described as the 'sum total of the universe including humanity'. i.e. the material universe can be divided into solid (Earth), liquid (Water), and vapour (Air), and these three are transformed one into the other, through the agency of energy (Fire).

In humans, solid food is digested into the bloodstream and turned into energy and the breath of life, as well as invisible thoughts, memories, images. In this way nature corresponds to human nature. In their context *Earth*, *Air*, and *Water* are aspects of spatial reality while *Fire* symbolizes the process of time.

Basic Qualities (*State*)

To be able to identify an energy pattern it is necessary to be able to recognise the inherent nature of the elemental forces which may predominate. A helpful definition of any force is that: " *A force expresses itself in a form which it has concentrated according to its' nature and meaning.*"

Water exists naturally in three states i.e. Solid, liquid and gas, but is most often defined by its liquid state e.g. a transparent, colourless, tasteless fluid. Some keywords describing the varieties of its form are: aqueous; damp; moist; dilute; humid; insipid; serous; flood; mist; saturate; bathe; whelm; deluge; drown; pour etc.

Liquid is the intermediary state between the solid and vapourous. Similarly, within the psyche there is a state between rigid attitudes and empty vacuous imaginings, where the life of the human can be blended with the material of the cosmos, affecting it, changing it, perfecting it. Liquid is further related to potential forms lying in the unconscious.

Air is defined as being atmosphere i.e. The mass of gas around the earth or a pervading influence in the environment or climate; an ambience or aura; feeling; mood; spirit or tone. Other words that describe the elemental state are e.g. Gaseous; ethereal; effervescent; vaporous; pneumatic; buoyant; light; animated and unsubstantial.

Vapour, steam, gases, smells, all that rise and dissolve invisibly into the sky:

The mind and imagination of humanity as well as their memories, like dissolving traces of former actions - together form an ethereal, or psychic, body: the living organism in close relationship with the cosmos.

The flow of breath unites the inner and outer realm, as well as being an invisible flow of mental energy which is of the same duration as our breathing i.e. stops when we stop breathing.

Fire has several definitions, those being: a mass of burning fuel; *the state of burning*; the evolution of light and heat during combustion; the combination of one chemical element with another, when reduced to gaseous solution produces heat, flame and light.

Words used to describe this state are e.g.: kindle; inflame; flicker; burning; smoulder; spark; blaze; glow; irritate; rouse; eruption; heat; combustion; conflagration; excite; enthusiasm; passion; radiance; spirit; vigour; impetuosity; inspiration; incite; stimulate and motivate.

Fire: The working-order of the world, the energy of the body and the life force of the cosmos. The fact that it can melt solids (e.g. Metals) into a state where they can be blended, may have contributed to making it an image of love and therefore union. Through the sun it was related to time which also transforms.

Earthy is the quality which is explained as: human; material; mortal; mundane; physical; secular; temporal; terrestrial and worldly and is given the qualities of stability; fixity; base; substantiality; tangibility and appears in nature as clay; dirt; ground; land; soil etc.

Earth: In the cosmos, substance, matter, nature. The flux of nature: the continuous change in nature reflects the same fluctuation of cause and effect in the lives of people. Nature continually breaks up, dissolves, flying into seeds, rotting down into earth, etc. and then reforming again, solid, freshly built. In the same way conscious attitudes get stale, rigid, and then break up into bits, dissolve and reform. *All that is solid, well-ordered. Stability.*

In some combinations the elements are incompatible (e.g. as when water puts out fire but these same two elements combine to foster the growth of plants as warmth of the sun and rain): This became an image of the way the opposite elements of life could be <u>mutually destructive, or wholly productive</u> of a third principle, if combined in a different way, as part of the process of living.

Another description of these elemental influences is that in general, their energy flow will consolidate, dissolve, transform and turn things back into themselves. They are invisible forces of energy (*but for their effects*, i.e. as the V.F. is described) that shape-change and consume everything in a cycle with its primary division into four.

Basic Qualities (*Faculties and Mobility*)

A further guide may be to explore the *faculties* associated with each element.

INTUITION: The quality or power of 'mind' which enables one to perceive the truth of anything without reasoning; a truth recognised i.e. **insight; instinct**.

Fire: might be described as the principle of *expansion* and *transmutation;* is related to the *spirit* and is associated with the **intuition**. *Fire* energises. *Fire* ignites and consumes. *Fire* is the element of transmutation - it brings about dramatic changes. *Fire* is the realm of spirituality, of sexuality and passion.

It expresses itself particularly in: Creativity; Enthusiasm and drive; Extroverted behaviour and Versatility.

The polarity is (+) because it is <u>active</u> and *penetrating.*

EMOTION: An excited state of feeling

Water: might be described as the principle of *fluidity. Water* flows, and takes the shape of whatever contains it, and it finds its own level. It is related to the *soul* and is associated with **emotions** and **feelings**. *Water* dispenses. *Water* is fluid and constantly changing. It is the element of absorption and germination. *Water* is the realm of love and emotions.

It expresses itself particularly in: Imagination; Sympathy and Understanding; Sensitivity and Introverted behaviour.

The polarity of Water is (-), because it is <u>mutable</u> (i.e. Changeable; inconstant; variable) and *receptive.*

SENSATION: Pertaining to the bodily faculties of perception or feeling i.e. Taste; touch; smell; hearing; sight; proprioception.

Earth: might be described as the principle of *inertia* and *stability.* Earth is the taking of form, the appearance of solidity. It is related to the *physical body* and is associated with **sensations**. *Earth* contains. *Earth* is stability. *Earth* is the foundation of the Elements and the one we are most comfortable with because it is stable, solid and dependable. *Earth* is the realm of abundance and prosperity. It expresses itself particularly in: Practicalities; Patience and Persistence; Sensuality; Conservatism; Cautiousness.

The polarity of Earth is (-) because it is fixed; fertile, nurturing and fruitful.

INTELLECT: The faculty of the human mind which receives ideas and deduces conclusions from them; the power to judge and comprehend; the reasoning faculty.

Air: is related to the *mind* and is associated with **thinking** - with **thoughts and ideas**. Air stimulates. Air is clear and uncluttered. Air provides impetus. Air is the realm of thought and the intellect.

It expresses itself particularly in: Mental and Verbal communication; Ideas; Social popularity.

The polarity of Air is (+) because it is active (also mutable and fixed) and expansive.

The Four Humours

The theory of the four *humours* is said to have originated with *Alcemon* of *Croton* in about 500BC. When he insisted that good health was dependant on a properly balanced mixture of the *humours*. This encompassed the fluids of the body i.e. Blood, phlegm, yellow and black bile. *Krasis*, or the ideal mixture, resulted in perfect health, although more often than not one of the *humours* predominated.

It was not until the ninth century AD the physician Johannitus invented the terms *Melancholici; Phlegmatici; Cholerici;* and *Sanquinei* to describe the effects of the *humours* of the body.

The *Melancholic* was said to have a predominance of black bile, which was described as cold and dry and associated with Autumn weather.

Phlegm had the qualities of being cold and moist and was associated with catarrhal affections often occurring in Winter.

The hot dryness of the Summer months was said to produce fevers of a bilious nature sometimes producing yellow skin supposedly due to the presence of too much yellow bile and was associated with the *Choleric.*

The Spring was said to bring a preponderance of dysentery and haemorrhages, this being the hot, moistness of the extraneous blood of the *Sanquinei.*

It is almost 700 years later before we find a much more comprehensive account of each *humour*. These appeared in " The Anatomy of Melancholy" by Robert Burton in 1621. In this work he paraphrased the writings of most of the great theoreticians. Burton focused on the *Melancholic humour,* believing that it was "... an inbred theory in all of us."

His description of the *Phlegmatic* type makes interesting reading when compared to some of the remedies often described in Homoeopathic Materia Medicas as such.

E.g. ".... Sleepy, dull, slow, blockish, ass-like......they are given to weeping and delight in water, ponds, pools, rivers.... They are pale of colour, slothful, apt to sleep, heavy, much troubled by the headache, continual meditation and muttering to themselves; they dream of waters; that they are in danger of drowning and fear such things. They are fatter than others .... apt to spit, more troubled with rheum.... and have their eyes still fixed on the ground."

Here the clear connection with *element* of Water is apparent.

As can be seen from this distilled information from authors of ancient times, including Aristotle, Hippocrates, Theophrastus and Galen: each of the *humours* can be associated for the most part to each of the four elements

i.e. *Phlegmatic* - WATER; *Choleric* - FIRE; *Melancholic* - EARTH; and not quite so obvious; the animated and buoyant *Sanquine* with AIR.

The Four Temperaments

(Adapted from 'Between Form and Freedom,' Betty Staley, 1988

Introduction

Here we introduce a deeper and more contemporary understanding of what the four humours are. Under the light of Rudolph Steiner's Anthroposophy, they become 'The Temperaments' and the characteristic descriptions are also explored from the homeopathic perspective in terms of the way those characteristics are considered when trying to identify **the essence** of the patient and in order to repertorise and come up with an accurate prescription, using individualising characteristics.

After birth there are four energetic bodies involved in the process of continuing growth i.e.:

The *Etheric* body consisting of formative and growth forces is said to have a quality of levity;

The *Astral* body consists of the intellectual forces or Consciousness;

The *Ego* is concerned with the Will; and lastly the *Physical* body through which these forces operate and is considered relatively heavy and inactive.

The forces of the *Astral* and *Ego* are not inherited but unite with the *Physical* and the *Etheric* bodies at birth. Their nature is to overcome and destroy the inherited forces in order that the child may maintain individuality - a battle frequently fought out in typical childhood illnesses.

The **_temperament_** is formed by the psychological space in which the individuality and the hereditary meet and influence each other.

There is a need to play out the temperament which possesses us in childhood or we may remain possessed by it, into adulthood. Even so, there is often a predominance of the characteristics of one _temperament_ with shades of the others in adulthood itself.

There are _four_ _temperaments_ named after the ancient _humours_ i.e. _Melancholic, Sanguine, Choleric_ and _Phlegmatic_.

There are certain characteristics of mind, body and emotions associated with each:

Physical Features

Melancholic

Often tall, slender and lean appearance with an impression of heaviness. There may often be a droop to the shoulders and face; the limbs hanging heavy with the head bent.

They have a measured and steady walk but the steps lack firmness and seem to drag them along. The voice is soft and restrained and because they often hold back they may mumble or be unable to complete sentences. When making decisions the voice is often toneless or when being stubborn they emit deep sighs. There is a general air of sadness about the _melancholic_.

Sanguine

Often of balanced proportions and are slender and supple. They have a light springing step and can have fine co-ordination. The face is alert and expressive with twinkling eyes. Both their features and their moods change easily; their gestures are quick and varied with much expression. They talk for the sake of talking and often bubble and chatter. They have a general air of lightness.

Phlegmatic

Physically the *Phlegmatic* has a roundness of body shape and are often heavily built and flabby. They tend to move slowly and have an unhurried, easy walk though their movements can be clumsy. They resist haste and are sluggish. The eyes often appear dull as they tend to turn inwards. They will look calm and appear aloof. They have a clear voice; the speech is correct but unmodulated.

Choleric

The *Choleric* is of short, stocky build with a muscular appearance of firmness and solidity. They are often full of energy and restlessness. They are firmly rooted with a stomping walk, sometimes with a staggering gait. They often pace and can appear poised for action. They tend to dig their heels in showing a tendency to stubbornness.

Their gestures are short, assertive and confident. The voice is strong, blustery. They tend to shout and may sound commanding.

Generalities

Melancholic

These individuals have a <u>general lack of vitality</u>. There is a sensitiveness to how things feel and they can complain about feelings of *tightness* about the neck or waist or be bothered by the scratchiness of fabric or the annoying little detail of clothes.

They can often give a long list of discomforts and every little ache is magnified. The *melancholic* takes impressions deeply into the soul affecting the physical body and may consequently suffer stomach and headaches (especially children; adults would have a deeper disturbance) This may lead to them missing events due to illness.

They are slow to awaken and don't like to be rushed. They can be fussy about food and like it prepared in a particular way. There is a dietary preference for sweets and new tastes are not easily acquired.

Sanguine

The individual with a preponderance of the *sanguine* temperament lives strongly in the Nervous System. They tend to bounce back from minor ailments. They can drop off to sleep no problem and go into a deep sleep or conversely will suffer from over-activity holding off sleep. The sanguine individual feels nourished by sleep and is an early waker.

Generally, they are open to change and adaptable to changes in routine etc. There can be an inability to relax, which may lead to hyperactivity. They love the changeability of life but can be vulnerable to fads of e.g. fashion. They like many foods and can be capricious with their diet, tending to eat small quantities and nibble at food.

Phlegmatic

The *phlegmatic* lacks vitality. They would rather stay still and not be bothered to exert themselves. They tend to resist change, sometimes to the point of defying it. Physical satisfaction is felt in enjoying life in a sluggish fashion. Their sluggishness has its' own momentum but inertia can become a problem and they tend to move slowly. Their needs are the basics of life; to be fed, cared for and a comfortable place to sleep. These needs indicating that physical wellbeing is a predominant influence. As well as sleep, food is also important to the *phlegmatic*, eating large full meals, which are preferably regular along with regular bedtime hours.

The stability of the *phlegmatic* can bring balance to situations.

Choleric

Filled with energy, the *choleric* wakes easily and plans the day. Their restless movement can result in a tendency to become over-extended or burned out.

Their sense of wellbeing is strong and they take pride in being healthy. They are not fussy about food, but they particularly like crunchy or spicy foods. They eat heartily but do not over-indulge.

Mental Features

(Memory, Perception, Understanding)

Melancholic

In the *Melancholic* the memory goes very deep. Information can be drawn out slowly, being poor re-callers at first. They tend to hang on to details but may miss the main points. They observe the world, giving everything thoughtful consideration i.e. thinkers who are attentive and like to figure out the details. Therefore, they are exhaustive researchers. This also lends the attribute of being meticulous in following directions and generally they have a perfectionist approach to life. *Melancholic's* are excellent conversationalists about issues and events contributing intelligent perceptions but may have a tendency to fixed ideas and have difficulty adjusting to change or may respond too slowly or inappropriately. They consider their routines as very important and for the *melancholic*, stimulation comes from within.

They can be prone to recurrent nightmares.

Sanguine

The memory of the *sanguine* is able to grasp information quickly but is also quick to forget. They find it hard to concentrate on anything for long and make what seem random statements, as if flitting from idea to idea with little depth of thought. They exaggerate freely.

Impressions jump quickly into imaginations and they tend to live in the images; pictures coming and going in the mind and feelings, sometimes being at their mercy. Fantasy and reality can grow confused and as children often have imaginary companions.

The sanguine is easily distracted, easily bored, lacking persistence and leaving much undone. They have many interests, which are short-lived but there is usually one serious interest which underlies the chaos and frenzy. Their difficulty in concentrating makes them forgetful, any projects looking carelessly done with writing all over the place. They lack a sense of form and development, seeking stimulation from without.

They develop calmness as they grow into adulthood but often retain the quality of the 'eternal child'.

Phlegmatic

The *phlegmatic* is a thoughtful individual who often struggles with memory of details. Nevertheless, they do have a good memory and learn slowly. This can give the misleading impression of being unintelligent. The *phlegmatic* needs time to work things out, and slowly come to a sensible decision. They need to put everything in order. They remember events that occur at particular times of the year e.g. birthdays. Once they get started it is difficult to stop them and given a task they will keep on until it is completed. The *phlegmatic* individual is a careful worker who can be organised or conversely their work will be in total disorder. They are cautious and will not go ahead with new plans or take risks. They seldom use initiative and although they have good ideas, they are unwilling to bring them forth. They like to follow orders and enjoy doing things well to the final detail but will avoid changing to new tasks using willpower to resist. They like repetition and simple tasks that take little mental exertion and are considered reliable. They tend to be practical people and feel satisfied when everything has its rightful place and purpose.

They like to dream and at times can find it hard to focus and are said to be asleep to much of the outer world. Stimulation comes from within. Images of past deeds are buried below the surface. They can be great listeners but have little to say.

The *phlegmatic* is comfortable with routine and predictability and enjoys the customs and rituals of life; therefore, respectability and acceptance are important to them.

Choleric

The individual with a predominantly *choleric* temperament is apt to scan the environment with restless eyes. They are not easily distracted and are glad to tackle jobs with a desire to get things done in order to move on to the next task or will direct attention to the details. They are perfectionists and like things done their way to the extent that they will at times re-do or re-organise others' work. They are people who come up with good ideas but everything has to be their idea. They are natural leaders and good organisers making many plans. They are generally reliable once a task has been taken on and will stoically endure setbacks. The *choleric* needs time to integrate requests to change and have to do it first in private because saving face is important.

They are the 'movers and shakers' in life who need space around them. Their stimulation comes from without.

Emotional Features

Melancholic

Often quiet and withdrawn individuals, they can become serious and resigned. With a tendency to become engrossed in the past, they remember insults and injuries and no matter how small, believe they are meant to hurt. Due to a lack of humour, they are easily teased and annoyed often responding viciously at once or conversely they will wait to strike back. They worry about everything and are self-involved, withdrawing and feeling resentful if someone tries to draw them out; or feel nervous if they feel their inner life is being probed. They find it difficult to say 'sorry' or admit mistakes and at times make blunt comments, which hurt others.

The *melancholic* may brood over deaths, marital problems etc. and will blame themselves for years. There is a general tendency to assume blame for others, feeling guilty and punishing themselves.

Melancholics are loners who are not eager to meet new people, believing that they are unique and will cultivate a sense of separateness. This may lead to loneliness, cynicism and a sense of rejection, but they can become committed to the service of others or would make conscientious leaders. They lack confidence and are slow to make friends being something of a perfectionist. When they do finally trust someone, their loyalty goes deep. They can be kind and gentle when their sympathy is aroused but also seek sympathy, which they do receive. The sharing of internal misery gives them pleasure. They respond easily to hurt or sick animals, caring for them meticulously.

The *melancholic* individual imagines catastrophes in the world and in their bodies and can become exhausted by the weight of the world. They tend to avoid worrying anxieties and find making decisions very painful. Their reactions are often shallow but nevertheless, emotional problems have a strong effect on *melancholics*; they feel afraid and want to know what to expect. They crave security therefore routine is important to them.

They are afraid of new experiences, their resistance to change masking fear. They want order in their life and their belongings, sometimes to an extreme. They can be quite spiteful if their things are disturbed by others. Consequently, they feel that the world disturbs their order; they are not at fault.

The *melancholic* needs clear goals and have a strong artistic sense which needs encouragement.

Sanguine

The individual with a predominance of the *sanguine* temperament likes to meet new people; sociability is their forte. They want to be in the centre of what's going on and will dress in outfits, which provide an image. They enjoy conviviality and make many friends and are fun to be with though they can become hyper active. Their moods change easily therefore it is often difficult to know where one stands with them. They find it difficult to maintain any depth in their relationships and can be unreliable, often using charm to excuse themselves. They feel guilt only fleetingly, accepting rebuke and moving on by brushing it off. They don't hold grudges and are considered pleasant and accommodating; big hugs and smiles coming readily. Seeing only goodness in the world, they are easily duped or led astray.

The *sanguine* experiences difficulty in establishing habits and tend to be surrounded by good-natured chaos. The emotional ups and downs are the keynote of their life. They avoid getting down to anything serious and are often seen as superficial. Sometimes being impatient, forgetful and irresponsible.

They are the 'life and soul' of the party, being a good joke teller and entertainer etc. with a tendency to make an adventure of life.

They are adaptable to changes and are very receptive to every new thing, seeming to let sorrow pass them by.

Their strongest motivating force is their love for the people around them and will do things for the person, not the deed. They are very co-operative people, wanting, even craving lots of attention and enjoy sharing and being overly generous. They need warmth and encouragement and innocence is a key quality of the *Sanguine*.

Phlegmatic

The *Phlegmatic* individual is good-natured, kind, thoughtful, but will remain aloof. They have a pleasant disposition, tending to go along with what is happening. They are likeable and well-mannered but their pleasantness comes from a desire not to be disturbed, not necessarily from feeling deeply for others.

They are easy-going with a resistance to haste or compulsion; they are suspicious of or feel sad for busy people. The *phlegmatic* will resist change for change's sake, considering it a waste of energy. They use their willpower to resist, exerting stubbornness and defying any change. There is a tendency to become sullen and moody but they try not to let anyone see it as they don't like to make waves. They are usually seen as co-operative, rule abiding and pleasant. Equally, they can also become sarcastic but usually not to another's face and will find ways to hurt those perceived as being 'on their case'. They dwell on irritations, taking them more seriously than others.

The *phlegmatic* is shy and introspected, lacking self-confidence and being modest about good ideas will not express an opinion for fear of being rebuked. Acceptance is important to them and they want to be recognised and appreciated.

They are amenable to whatever goes on as long as they feel comfortable; liking it when there are calm people around. They are easy people to be with, not exciting, but they like excitable people to be around so that they can experience situations without demands being made on them. They don't like to be pushed into anything. They are not affected by chaos as long as their personal needs are met.

They can be careful, organised workers but conversely can be in complete disorder.

Their preoccupation with the inner world can strengthen them but they may become self-focused and overly concerned with illness and disability.

The *phlegmatic* is known to be dependable, loyal, reliable, steadfast, honest and truthful.

Choleric

The individual with a predominantly *choleric* temperament wants to appear tough and independent refusing to show weakness or vulnerability and will stoically endure setbacks. They can be self-centred, pushy and demanding. It's important for them to be the first, the biggest or the toughest. Life is a competition with others or with themselves and they seem to be always fighting towards a goal. They have an underlying desire to prove themselves; to succeed.

If they feel they need to intimidate others they will justify it with their need to get things done. They are bossy and move easily into positions of authority. Because they feel mastery over situations and people they are natural leaders. These strong leadership qualities easily sway others. Their way is the best and they have the energy to do it though they will start plans and leave others to do the work.

The *choleric* dislikes criticism, finding it difficult to admit they are wrong and will aggressively trade insults if challenged. They will challenge others and have something to say about everything but find it difficult to take what they give. They can become stubborn and argumentative and like the excitement of argument but may be hurt and carry a grudge for a long time. In fact, the *choleric* can be vicious if their honour is attacked, defending the right and will battle to the 'death'. They need to be stood up to or they will continue to bully others.

They understandably have difficulty in accepting blame and can be quick to put it on to others. Wanting everything their own way; will throw tantrums and cause a ruckus if they don't get it. Seeking glory, they will gain it in whatever way; positive or negative. Clearly they are happy with a sense of power and do not share the glory well.

They are convinced the world is headed downhill and they have to sort it out but they can feel impatient and burdened by life. They want recognition that they are indispensable so tend to accept responsibility easily but need to prioritise or will become exhausted or burned-out by their sometime extreme tendency to say 'yes' (or 'no') to everything. They are therefore generally reliable.

The *cholerici* don't like to appear afraid and will cover it up by working. They want to do the right thing and will be able to accept the pain and realisation of error and are deeply saddened if they hurt someone, wanting to make amends; but they need time to do it in their own way because saving face is important to them.

If they feel needed, they can give their heart and soul. They will carry others' burdens literally and figuratively and do have a wish to be helpful and serve others.

If they feel supported, their sense of humour blossoms, they can even laugh at themselves. They are then seen to be sensitive and generous.

Cholerics with a *sanguine* tendency are easily pulled this way and that and will fight themselves.

Those with a *melancholic* tendency can become self-pitying and bitter or devoted and loving if supported.

Each temperament is associated with an element:

Choleric – *Fire*

Phlegmatic – *Water*

Melancholic – *Earth*

Sanguine - **Air**

The Polychrests

What is a Polychrest remedy?

A polychrest remedy in homeopathy is a remedy that has many uses. In other words, the remedy has the ability to treat many ailments. There are approximately 100 polychrests (out of thousands of remedies) with this ability.

There is no standard and final list of such remedies. Each practitioner makes their own list depending on the type of cases received and needs of his/her clinic.

For example, most of the remedies described by Dr. Margret Tyler in her book on *Drug Pictures* can be considered as ideal examples of polychrest remedies.

It has been stated that a polychrest is a remedy whose provings and clinical applications show that it has many widespread uses, covering a wide variety of mental, emotional and physical symptomatology.

Dr. H. C. Allen says a polychrest is a remedy which affects all or nearly all the tissues of the body, has a wide variation in symptoms and its curative power reaches deep into the anatomy ... is equally useful in acute and chronic disorders, but in chronic work may prove curative or ameliorative when all other methods fail.

How do we identify a polychrest in clinic?

The polychrest can be identified from various perspectives e.g.

+ Sphere of action
+ Mental emotional picture
+ Characteristic symptoms either mental or physical
+ General modalities

This can still be a problem for homoeopaths that stumble when having to select a correct polychrest for a patient. As homeopaths grow with experience, our knowledge of remedies also grows. However, it can be difficult to maintain an intimate knowledge of even the polychrest remedies. The main reason for this is that many polychrests have a similar features e.g. Phosphorous and Causticum. This is a constant challenge for all homeopaths. For beginner homeopaths, it can be both an advantage and a disadvantage to not have preconceived ideas of the importance of any one remedy. To see all remedies as equally important can be liberating. It can also be profoundly confusing.

When one should avoid using a polychrest?

Generally, it should be avoided when there is no **essence** to help one find the remedy. Ideally, the case should have a clear **essence**, totality, confirming keynotes and confirming general and causation symptoms.

The ideal case is not what we often see before us and for various reasons one or more of these categories may be missing. In such a situation it is best to wait for symptoms to develop. However, I would like to advise that in a very few cases when **the essence** is missing, it must not prejudice you into avoiding all polychrest remedies. In fact, it is still just as likely that a polychrest remedy will be indicated.

Learning to identify **the essence** using elemental circles as explained and demonstrated here can help clear up both that importance confusion and the hesitation to prescribe polychrests.

Polychrest Remedies: Nat Mur: Natrum Muriaticum (Nat-m.) is prepared from common table salt, yet, in potency, treats a large range of acute and chronic problems

ESSENTIAL EXPRESSIONS OF THE VITAL FORCE (The Polychrests)

NATRUM MURIATICUM (Salt)   *Essence* = **Exchange/ Bi-Polar**
Diagram 1 - Affinities; Organs/ Systems of the Body
Modalities; Exciting Causes.

(HOT)

FIRE
SPLEEN (Liver)
HEART & CIRCULATORY SYSTEM
NERVOUS SYSTEM; EYES < *Exertion;*
E.C. Fit of Passion; Acid Food
< Heat of Sun; warm, stuffy rooms.   < Violent

< Night   < Coition   Emotions

Sunset < ———————————————— < **Sunrise**

< Moving; Least Exertion   *<Sympathy/Consolation*
SKIN (*ERUPTIONS* = **Dry**———   **Weepy**)   **EMOTIONS**
SKELETAL SYS. (=**Rigid**———   **Rheumatics**)   LYMPHATICS
EARTH *(DRY)*   **WATER***(WET)*
DIGESTIVE SYS.(=**Nausea**———**Vomiting**) REPRODUCTIVE SYS.
E.C. Bread; Fat; *Salt (=* **Constipation**———**Diarrhoea**) URINARY SYS.
(Desires & Averse Salt)   < Seaside & >Seaside; < **Dampness**
EMACIATION   *CHILLY*   EXCRETORY ORGANS
RETENTION   < Draughts; Mental Exertion **E.C.** Loss of Fluids
> Rest   >Open Air; >Deep Breathing;   **E.C. Grief, Shock, Fright**
<Mental Exertion   **E.C. Disappointment**   < Morning
Tendency to Colds
NERVOUS SYSTEM
LUNGS
AIR
(COLD)

ACUTES of **NAT. MUR.**

Pulsatilla	Rhus Toxicendron
Ignatia (Also Chronic)	Bryonia
Staphisagria	Sepia (Also Chronic)
Gelsemium	

The *melancholic* (see *The Four Temperaments)* base to the NAT.MUR.
patients' character supplies them with a deep memory which in the child is
poor at first, needing drawn out slowly. They seem to observe the world and in
keeping with their bi-polar nature may think themselves unique and therefore
cultivate a sense of separateness. They are often serious adults and children,
who are shy and introverted (**Sepia**), and may give an impression of heaviness.
As children they are often well - behaved, responsible, obedient and ultra co-
operative, in order to avoid rejection by parents. The child is very sensitive to
disapproval therefore afraid they will not please. If successful in this early
precursor to a manipulative trait, we see the tense smile break into a wonderful
grin, which transforms their often, pale face, the skin appearing thin.
When their sympathies are aroused, the NAT.MUR. childs sensitivity
becomes gentleness and kindness. They are easily able to respond to hurt or
sick animals. Making friends their own age will take longer due to their lack of
confidence and they are often 'loners'. They take impressions deep into the
soul, which manifests in the physical body as stomach or head aches. The
headaches can be **excited** by the heat of the sun or more fundamentally by
emotional shocks such as grief, fright or disappointment. The growing child
may worry much, especially at bedtime and can be prone to recurrent
nightmares.
They are apt to blame themselves for others' actions resulting in guilt and are
wont to punish themselves.
The child may collapse hysterically on hearing of e.g. parental divorce,
weeping with an inability to say why. *Ignatia* (see *Diagram 3*) may be better
indicated in such an instance to deal with the acute grief.
The growing child or youth finds it difficult to say 'sorry' or to admit mistakes;
and as they grow older this becomes a pattern of withdrawal and defence in
the form of emotional barriers or in a tendency to arguments and quarrels with
the fixed idea that they are 'right' (**Sepia).** These emotional barriers can
intensify their feeling of isolation. Their sensitivity predisposes them to easy
offence (**Sepia)** and vulnerable to any criticism, deserved or not.
Again revealing their bi-polar and exchanging essence is the easy conviction
that perceived insults and injuries, no matter how small are meant to hurt.
They neither forget, nor forgive. These grievances will be carried with them
into adulthood, as will grief of a deeper nature e.g. deaths; including those of
favoured pets.
The emotional barrier can result in a 'don't touch me' attitude, often projected
onto family, especially parents; compounding their feelings of unworthiness.
The formerly affectionate and well-behaved child can become moody and
unhappy, consequently pushing away what they crave most; love and security.
The abruptness and irritability (**Sepia)** can manifest here even though the
young adolescent will try to control it.

They may become prone to alternating diarrhoea and constipation (*see Diagram 2*) in their efforts at retention of anger and loss of control (*Exchange*).

Colic may be concommitant with these symptoms, indicative of their worrying, fearful natures and over time this may deepen into a *chronic* state or appear as an *acute of the chronic* picture of 'Ilietis'.

At this point, as the patient requiring NAT.MUR. moves into adulthood proper, the area of relationships involving intimacy and sexual relations becomes more of a focus. Their difficulty in coping with and sustaining relationships becomes more noticeable. Their sympathetic and receptive nature makes them good listeners with insight from a distance, able to offer advice and support to friends, but their own vulnerability is hidden behind a 'hard' façade (**Sepia**) which holds and represses their own deep emotions. They are unable to trust others and may become suspicious of their motives.

The patient may have an ability to manipulate and rationalise their feelings to avoid acknowledging and exposing deep hurts that they may have become quite attached to. They will often experience states of melancholy accompanied by an ensuing *chronic* constipation occurring every second day or at this stage, being prolonged over greater lengths of time.

An increasing feeling of rejection may be felt. This is due both to their inability to open up and share themselves aswell as to the fact that because of the vibration they are projecting to others of suspicion, mistrust etc. they will be left alone. It is possible that after discords the patient when feeling angry will retain fixed ideas, which cling and prevent sleep, sometimes producing feelings of revenge. Though due to an enduring degree of sensitivity and unwillingness to hurt others, they will be blunt and possess a sharp tongue (**Sepia**), but will repress the sharp retort and bottle up their feelings of anger, hurt or ambiguity. At the physical level, the NAT.MUR patient., after spending years holding onto resentments, may produce rheumatic stiffness of limbs and joints (see Diagram 6) and require an *'acute of the chronic'* remedy like **Rhus Tox.** to prevent ensuing *chronic* rigidity.

In a deeply *chronic* state of the Nervous System (e.g. Multiple Sclerosis) further into the disease process, the patient may present with *'Acute'* paralysis of limbs and dysfunctional proprioception e.g. parts seem too short; numbness on one side; paralysis of fingers. This process manifesting at much deeper levels, better resonates with *Alumina* as the appropriate *chronic* remedy (i.e. *chronic* to **Sepia** and NAT.MUR. See below)

Developmental Stages

In Diagram 1 we can already see the basic attributes and qualities in the elemental circle. It also illustrates the affinities mainly in the remedy picture (vibrational pattern) of the constitutional presentation. At the bottom of the diagram, noted are remedies useful for both acute and chronic states in the Natrum Muriaticum constitution i.e. seven other related remedies (Ignatia, Staphisagria, Gelsemium, Rhus Tox, Pulsatilla, Bryonia, Sepia)

Also included are time modalities, mental states, emotions, systems of the body. Identifying the nature of the fundamental cause, the nature of the energy inherent in a remedy, pathological conditions or miasmatic expressions will become apparent as we move through the better indicated remedies in the development process.

1. Basic Attributes
    The initial stage of development is encompassed in learning the Basic attributes of the four elements in relation to their position on the elemental Circle. These attributes cover both modalities and some General symptoms of any particular remedy. It is useful to use four remedy pictures throughout the stages in order to illustrate how attributes etc. correlate to their elemental energy. Each remedy picture is chosen for its predominance of one energy pattern e.g. PULSATILLA-WATER etc.

By learning these basic attributes and beginning to explore the nature and form of the inherent energy in each element, one becomes able to form an understanding of how to recognise those attributes in relation to any remedy or patient (i.e. a vibrational pattern)

The basic diagram of the circle (as in Diagram 1) and some variations are featured.

EXPRESSION	AIR	EARTH	WATER	FIRE
Sensation	COLD	DRY	WET	HOT
Direction	NORTH	WEST	EAST	SOUTH
Season	WINTER	AUTUMN	SPRING	SUMMER
Time	Midnight(NW) (12-6am)	Sunset(SW) (6pm-12am)	Sunrise(NE) 6am-12pm	Midday(SE) (12pm-6pm
Colour	BLUE	BROWN	YELLOW	RED

Levels of Acutes

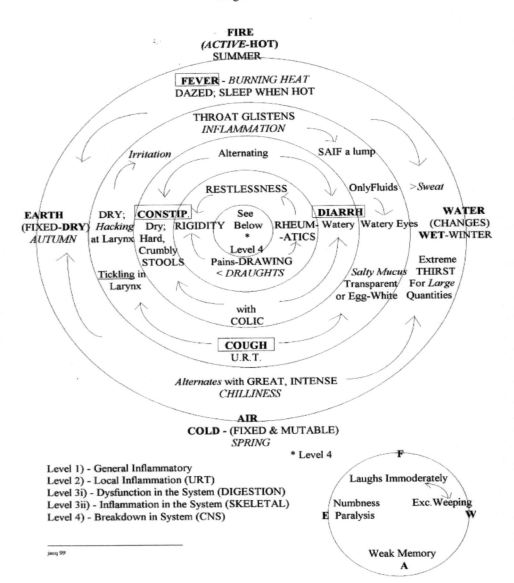

FIRE
(ACTIVE-HOT)
SUMMER

FEVER - *BURNING HEAT*
DAZED; SLEEP WHEN HOT

THROAT GLISTENS
INFLAMMATION

Irritation Alternating SAIF a lump

RESTLESSNESS OnlyFluids >*Sweat*

EARTH DRY; CONSTIP. See DIARRH WATER
(FIXED-**DRY**) *Hacking* Dry; RIGIDITY Below RHEUM- Watery Watery Eyes (CHANGES)
AUTUMN at Larynx Hard, * -ATICS WET-WINTER
Crumbly Level 4
STOOLS Pains-DRAWING Extreme
Tickling in < *DRAUGHTS* *Salty Mucus* THIRST
Larynx Transparent For *Large*
or Egg-White Quantities

with
COLIC

COUGH
U.R.T.

Alternates with GREAT, INTENSE
CHILLINESS

AIR
COLD - (FIXED & MUTABLE)
SPRING

* Level 4

Level 1) - General Inflammatory
Level 2) - Local Inflammation (URT)
Level 3i) - Dysfunction in the System (DIGESTION)
Level 3ii) - Inflammation in the System (SKELETAL)
Level 4) - Breakdown in System (CNS)

F
Laughs Immoderately
Numbness Exc.Weeping
E Paralysis W
Weak Memory
A

jacq 99

54

In the discussion on both the elements and the vital force, there was mention of the importance of both the digestive and respiratory systems. Here are examples of levels of acute conditions in both these systems illustrating the downward/ deepening nature of the disease process and conversely, indications for the healing process when initiated with homeopathic treatment

Digestive System 1

Levels of Acute & Disease Process in the Digestive System

Halitosis: Bad smelling breath from mouth or lungs
Aetiology:
Lack of Dental Hygiene(M.C.)
Oral Infection(E.C.)
Infected Sinuses-Local Inflamm(Minor Sys)
Infected Lungs-Local Inflamm(MO)
Lung Abcesses-Pathology(Suppuration
(Major Organ)

Hering's Law of Cure states that
Symptoms move from:
Above Downwards
Within outwards
Major organs & systems
to Minor organs & systems
In reverse order of Appearance

Stomatitis: Inflammation of mucous Membranes of mouth. May involve gums, lips, tongue
Aetiology: Dry Mouth, Lack of Vit.B Complex, Allergy, Infection eg. Thrush, Chicken Pox, (FC) Measles, Herpes Zoster (shingles) –
Local Inflammation

Colic: Griping pain, diarrhoea etc.
Aetiology:Various causes including:
Faulty digestion; poisoning; infection
Dysfunction

CardioSpasm or Achalasia of Oesophagus: Failure of lower oesophageal sphincter
Aetiology: Faulty or reversed peristalsis(PNS)
Undigested food regurgitates (may go into Lungs) *Dysfunction*

Hiatus Hernia: Widening/weakening/ Opening of stomach wall into thoracic cavity *Aietiology*: Injury, Miasmatic FC
Dysfunction

Coeliac Disease: abnormal mucosa in small intestine decreasing surface area of absorption *Aetiology*: Gluten allergy?
with weight loss, diarrhoea; pale, voluminous stool; anaemia
Dysfunction

I.B.S. or Spastic Colon: Bowel habits disturbed by Diarrhoea &/or constipation
Pellet or ribbon-like stool with or without mucus, Painless diarrhoea in morning, f.as if 'Never get done' in rectum; rumbling, headache; tiredness.
Dysfunction

Hepatitis:
Inflammation of Liver-reduces functioning of liver cells & blocks bile ducts by swelling of tissues- *Aetiology*:
Infection, alcohol poisoning, toxins.
Inflammation of Major Organ

Digestive System 2- Fill in the Aetiology

Gallstones: stones in Gall bladder
Or ducts
Aetiology:

Dysfunction in System

Gastro Enteritis-
Inflammation of stomach &
intestinal lining. Aetiology:

Inflammation of major organs/system

Jaundice-Concentration of bilirubin
localised bile) deposited in skin &
sclerotics   Aetiology:

Dysfunction in System

CrohnsDisease:inflammation of
bowel-lesions-(may present as
Appendicitis) colicky pain/nausea/rumbling.

Aetiology:
Dysfunction ⟶ Structural change

Ulcer(Peptic): erosion of GIT
mucosa-due to exposure to gastric acid
Epigastric burning/gnawing pain

vomiting/haemetesis(coffee granules)
Melaena(black stools); bloody stools
Pyloric Stenosis(F.C. & Complications)
Aetiology:
Structural change

Ulcerative Colitis-continual inflammation
throughout affected part of colon or
bowel
Deep or superficial ulceration. Aetiology:

Structural Change

Respiratory System

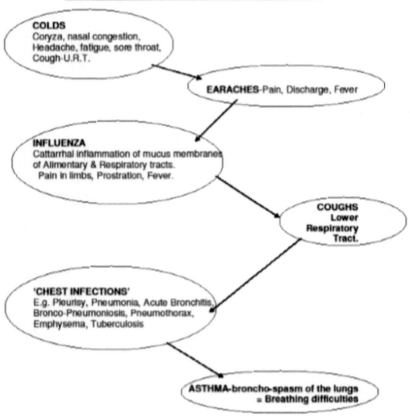

Levels of Acute & Disease Process in Respiratory System

COLDS
Coryza, nasal congestion,
Headache, fatigue, sore throat,
Cough-U.R.T.

EARACHES-Pain, Discharge, Fever

INFLUENZA
Cattarrhal inflammation of mucus membranes
of Alimentary & Respiratory tracts.
Pain in limbs, Prostration, Fever.

COUGHS
Lower
Respiratory
Tract.

'CHEST INFECTIONS'
E.g. Pleurisy, Pneumonia, Acute Bronchitis,
Bronco-Pneumoniosis, Pneumothorax,
Emphysema, Tuberculosis

ASTHMA-broncho-spasm of the lungs
= Breathing difficulties

Hering's Law of Cure states
that symptoms move:
From above downwards
From within outwards
From major to minor organs &
Systems
In reverse order of appearance

2. Basic Qualities

In this second stage, some of the inherent qualities of the individual elements will be explored in terms of the natural state and their ability to shift and change. Here the systems of the body are introduced in relation to the predominant elemental focus and type of expression. This takes into account affinities of particular remedies or predispositions of patients.

By adding these qualities to the attributes, one can now begin to recognise the relationship between remedies in terms of the elemental energy inherent in a particular vibrational pattern (symptom picture) involving identification of: Generals, Modalities and physical affinities.

The four faculties are introduced as a prelude to the differentiation of the elemental energy in certain mental and emotional states.
The humours are included as a comparison for individual expression of symptoms and mental states with discrimination as to their accuracy/differences to other psychological theories.

EXPRESSION	AIR	EARTH	WATER	FIRE
State	GAS	SOLID	LIQUID	HEAT
Mobility	FIXED & MUTABLE	FIXED	MUTABLE	ACTIVE
Faculties	INTELLECT	SENSES	EMOTIONS	INTUITION
Humours	SANGUINE	MELANCHOLIC	PHLEGMATIC	CHOLERIC
Systems of Body	CNS & RESPIR	SKELET&DIGEST	URIN/LYMPH & REPRODUCT	HEART/CIRC ENDOCRINE

3. Foundations of Individuality & Pathology

The third stage involves the discussion of the temperaments in relation to their predominant elemental focus and subsequent characteristics on both the General and Mental & Emotional levels. Certain keywords signifying the nature of the elemental energy are introduced, connecting with the previous attributes and qualities, which reflect a pathological tendency.

The miasms will be briefly discussed in relation to the elements and the nature of each **fundamental cause** will be explored to ascertain how its expression can be recognised within this schema.

As the characteristics of the individual and the basis of pathological expression in terms of energetic movement is grasped, one should then be able to assess the nature of change in the symptom picture and the type of inherent energy pattern manifesting in those symptoms seen to be needing cure.

The four patterns of distress (emotional anatomy) are introduced as an illustration of the energy utilised to maintain a pattern of defence, resulting in particular bodily state and shape both internally and externally.

As previously, a particular remedy and the previous two remedies will be shown to illustrate the vibrational patterns in relation to each other.

EXPRESSION	AIR	EARTH	WATER	FIRE
Temperament	SANGUINE	MELANCHOLIC	PHLEGMATIC	CHOLERIC
Nature of Energy	DIFFUSE	INHIBITING	FLOWING	DESTRUCTIVE
Nature of Fundamental Cause	LOSS/LACK OF BOUNDARIES	UNDER-FUNCTION	OVER-FUNCTION	DISINTEGRATION & DESTRUCTION
Miasms	CANCER	PSORA	SYCOTIC	SYPHILITIC
Patterns of Distress	COLLAPSED	RIGID	SWOLLEN	DENSE

Miasms

- An underlying condition which causes a gradually retrograde disease even though the acute manifestations were met by the homeopathic remedy. Hahnemann termed this deeper malady 'miasm'

- Constitution/inherited/inheritable tendency or trait

- Predisposition. Can be dormant –triggered by events/circumstances/environment

- The Tubercular miasm is regarded as psora-syphilitic in character.

- The **cancer miasm** is usually defined as a miasmatic constellation in which all four basic miasms are active.

CLC

Personality Types
of the Miasms

The mind and body work together as a unit and the disturbances are expressed in both spheres.

o <u>A – Psoric Miasm:</u> Highs and lows, struggles with the outside world, becomes apparent at times of stress. Lack of confidence, feeling of constant anxiety, fear, like they can't do it; insecurity, anxiety about the future but always having hope; mentally alert.

o <u>B – Sycotic Miasm:</u> Secretiveness, hide their weakness; tense, constantly covering up situations, fixed habits; suspicious, jealous, forgetful.

o <u>C – Syphilitic Miasm:</u> Strong, pessimistic view of life, cannot modify what is wrong; gives-up, destroys; no point in trying to adjust, sudden impulsive violence directed at themselves or others; distorted rigid ideas. Mental paralysis, mentally dull, suicidal, stupid, stubborn, and homicidal.

o <u>D – Tubercular Miasm:</u> Dissatisfaction, lack of tolerance, changes everything, does harmful things to one's self.

CLC

General Nature of the Miasms

- **A – Psoric Miasm:** Itching, burning, inflammation leading to congestion – philosopher, selfish, restless, weak, fears.

- **B – Sycotic Miasm:** Over production, growth like warts, condylomata, fibrous tissue, attacks internal organs, pelvis, and sexual organs.

- **C – Syphilitic Miasm:** Destructive, disorder everywhere, ulceration, fissures, deformities, ignorance, suicidal, depressed, memory diminished.

- **D – Tubercular Miasm:** Changing symptomology, vague, weakness, shifting in location, depletion, dissatisfaction, lack of tolerance, careless, "problem child", cravings that are not good for them.

4. Individual Expressions of Pathology

In this final stage of the development, the topics discussed may already be familiar to those with previous knowledge of Materia Medica and homeopathic philosophy. It will be discussed in relation to the elemental schema.

I will use the elemental circle to illustrate acute disease states and their corresponding remedies, which are related to the Nat mur constitutional presentation, including their Mental & Emotional experience in these acute states.

EMOTIONAL ANATOMY I

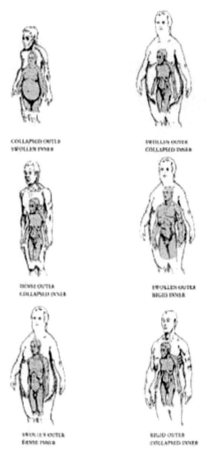

COLLAPSED OUTER
SWOLLEN INNER

SWOLLEN OUTER
COLLAPSED INNER

DENSE OUTER
COLLAPSED INNER

SWOLLEN OUTER
RIGID INNER

SWOLLEN OUTER
DENSE INNER

RIGID OUTER
COLLAPSED INNER

Ref:Emotional Anatomy; The structure of experience Stanley Keleman, Center Press 1985

EXPRESSION	AIR	EARTH	WATER	FIRE
Physical Presentation	CONGESTION	INFLAMMATION	SUPPURATION	ULCERATION
Levels of Disease	LOCAL INFLAMMATION/ MINOR ORGAN	GEN. INFLAMM RESPONSE	DYSF. MAJOR ORGAN/SYS	BREAKDOWN IN SYSTEM
Levels of Pathology	DYSFUNCTION	INFLAMMATION	STRUCTURAL CHANGE	NECROSIS
Emotional States	CONFUSION	FEAR & ANXIETY	SADNESS & WEEPING	ANGER & RAGE
Types of Manifestation	EPISODIC	ACUTE	ACUTE OF CHRONIC	CHRONIC

Note the integration of Exciting Causes and examples of deepening pathology in Diagram 3.

Types of Causes

*"Useful to the physician in assisting him to cure are the particulars of the most probable **exciting cause** of the acute disease as well as the most significant points in the complete history of the chronic disease, to enable him to **discover its fundamental cause, which is generally due to a chronic miasm.*** Samuel Hahnemann Aphorism 5 The Organon

Definitions of Acute and Chronic

To be sure that we understand what we mean by acute and chronic states, here is a definition of each:

ACUTE:a disease of rapid onset and short duration, which ends either in recovery or death. The symptoms are usually striking, and differ markedly from the patient's usual picture.

CHRONIC: In aphorism 78 of the Organon, Hahnemann defines chronic disease as those diseases which, when left to themselves, and 'unchecked by the employment of those remedies that are specific for them, always go on increasing and growing worse.'

When is an acute not a simple acute?

- If you are treating a condition that a patient has had on and off for a long time, such as hay fever or migraine headaches, you need to bear in mind an important difference between **a condition that periodically recurs** and which tends to go on for a long time and a **simple acute** such as an earache.

- This is what we call an **episodic** or an **acute of a chronic** state.

- In this situation you will select the remedy for the acute based on the totality of symptoms, as you will always do -

- But in order for the hay fever or the migraines or any other recurring state to truly be resolved the patient will need deeper chronic treatment from an experienced homeopath between their acute episodes.

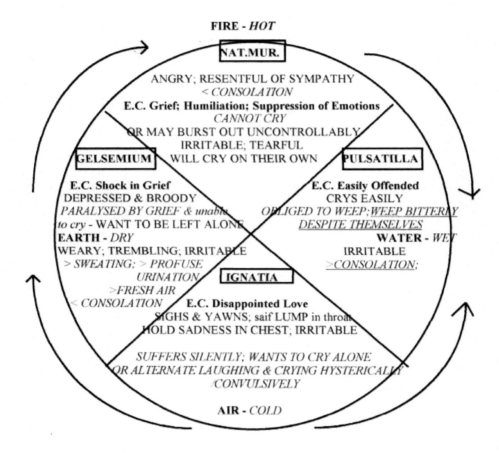

FIRE - *HOT*

NAT.MUR.

ANGRY; RESENTFUL OF SYMPATHY
< CONSOLATION
E.C. Grief; Humiliation; Suppression of Emotions
CANNOT CRY
OR MAY BURST OUT UNCONTROLLABLY
IRRITABLE; TEARFUL
WILL CRY ON THEIR OWN

GELSEMIUM

PULSATILLA

E.C. Shock in Grief
DEPRESSED & BROODY
PARALYSED BY GRIEF & unable
to cry - WANT TO BE LEFT ALONE
EARTH - *DRY*
WEARY; TREMBLING; IRRITABLE
> SWEATING; > PROFUSE
URINATION
>FRESH AIR
< CONSOLATION

E.C. Easily Offended
CRYS EASILY
OBLIGED TO WEEP;WEEP BITTERLY
DESPITE THEMSELVES
WATER - *WET*
IRRITABLE
>CONSOLATION;

IGNATIA

E.C. Disappointed Love
SIGHS & YAWNS; saif LUMP in throat
HOLD SADNESS IN CHEST; IRRITABLE

SUFFERS SILENTLY; WANTS TO CRY ALONE
OR ALTERNATE LAUGHING & CRYING HYSTERICALLY
/CONVULSIVELY

AIR - *COLD*

STAPHISAGRIA could also be used in an *Acute of* a *Chronic* state of Humiliation or Mortification in which the *NAT.MUR.* patient may turn to martyrdom or become 'noble--minded'. But they do not forget; they seethe silently. **Staphisagria** could encourage them to take action rather than become ill.

The following diagrams are ***Elemental Circles*** featuring:

- Diagram 4. Bryonia as Acute of the Chronic remedy for a Natrum Muriaticum constitution.
- Diagram 5. Nat Mur Mental & Emotional deepening levels of pathology
- Diagram 6. Rhus Tox, which can be required as Acute/ Acute of Chronic and Episodic for complaints in a Natrum Mur Constitution.
- Diagram 7. Sepia as a chronic remedy for the Natrum Mur constitution

Polychrest Remedies: Bryonia

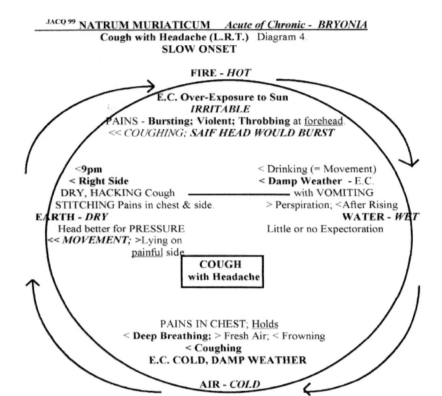

JACQ 99 **NATRUM MURIATICUM** *Acute of Chronic -* *BRYONIA*
Cough with Headache (L.R.T.) Diagram 4.
SLOW ONSET

FIRE - *HOT*

E.C. Over-Exposure to Sun
IRRITABLE
PAINS - Bursting; Violent; Throbbing at forehead.
<< *COUGHING; SAIF HEAD WOULD BURST*

<9pm
< Right Side
DRY, HACKING Cough
STITCHING Pains in chest & side.
EARTH - *DRY*
Head better for PRESSURE
<< *MOVEMENT;* >Lying on
painful side.

< Drinking (= Movement)
< **Damp Weather** - E.C.
———— with VOMITING
> Perspiration; <After Rising
WATER - *WET*
Little or no Expectoration

COUGH
with Headache

PAINS IN CHEST; Holds
< **Deep Breathing;** > Fresh Air; < Frowning
< **Coughing**
E.C. COLD, DAMP WEATHER

AIR - *COLD*

Bryonia is better suited at this level of the disease process in the *NAT.MUR.* patient, when the tendency to colds has developed into the Lower Respiratory Tract, because the symptom picture shows a deeper level of underfunctioning of the secretory processes, resulting in a lack of lubrication and discharge of fluids.ie One pole of the *NAT.MUR.* 's bi-polar nature. In *general*, the *NAT.MUR.* patient catches colds easily, but as their vitality ebbs further, the response of their Vital Force becomes slower; this rate of energy being more akin to that of **Bryonia**, a remedy of slow onset.

NAT.MUR. has dryness as a *general* feature, but at this level the lack of fluids is effecting dysfunction of a major organ ie. **Bryonia** < right **lung**.

In consideration of this relatively 'fixed' position, it is necessary to move the symptoms upwards and outwards from the respiratory system and to establish production of fluid; even if only to the level of local inflammation in the throat (see Diag.2); but which in the *NAT.MUR.* symptom picture has alternating dryness and expectoration of transparent or white mucus.

The **Bryonia** symptom picture may appear in the patient after a change of cold to warm weather

(exchange & polarity) or when there has been exposure to a damp chill. These **Exciting Causes** originating from the predispositions of the *NAT.MUR.* patient.
Both remedies experience thirst (*NAT.MUR.* having a dry mouth.) in compensation for the dryness elsewhere and when **Bryonia** is required as the *Acute of the Chronic* state, the thirst is more noticeable, the patient requiring large quantities, but drinking infrequently due to the aggravation from any movement.
Both remedies have a tendency to anger and in the acute presentation, the patient requiring **Bryonia** will be extremely irritable and want to be left alone when ill. Moroseness is evident in the acute symptom picture of **Bryonia**, along with their 'touchiness'.
The *NAT.MUR.* patient is often generally worse from sunrise to sunset (also 10am-3pm) and at night whilst the patient experiencing the headache concommitant with this cough is worse on getting up and can last all day; they are also aggravated at **9pm**.

Ideally, the aim of treatment of the *NAT.MUR.* chronic picture in the Respiratory Tract with remedies that are well indicated, would aim to shift the symptoms up from the L.R.T. to the larynx and then further up the U.R.T. to establish a more healthy expression of symptoms at the level of 'acute' colds. Here there would be a more fluid manifestation with increased vitality and a *Vital Force* which is quicker to respond.
Eg. Watery discharge from the eyes. Profuse,watery or white nasal catarrh which may drip down the back of the throat. There may be much sneezing and the lips of the patient may be dry and cracked. (Dryness moving up and out to the external mucous membranes from the deeper serous membranes in the lungs, seen in the patient requiring **Bryonia**.)
Further to this, a reduction in the tendency to 'catch colds easily' by strengthening the *Vital Force* even more would bring the patient closer to cure, keeping in mind that each patient may be different at one or other stage.

The **Bryonia** plant is in the gourd family. Native to Northern and Eastern Europe, this perennial climbing vine has white flowers, red berries, and a thick, fleshy root with a strong, bitter odour.

Individuality

- Another very important principle of homoeopathy is **individualising** the case.
- This means that each person is different, and so needs to be questioned very carefully for their **individual** symptoms.
- We cannot prescribe a homoeopathic remedy in a routine way as conventional medicine does.
- In homoeopathy, there is no such thing in as one remedy for everyone with the same disease.
- Each person has their own symptoms and needs a **unique** remedy especially chosen for them.

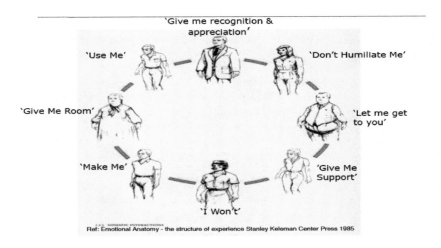

Ref: Emotional Anatomy - the structure of experience Stanley Keleman Center Press 1985

NATRUM MURIATICUM - *MENTAL & EMOTIONAL* - Levels of Pathology
Diagram 5

FIRE
(ACTIVE)

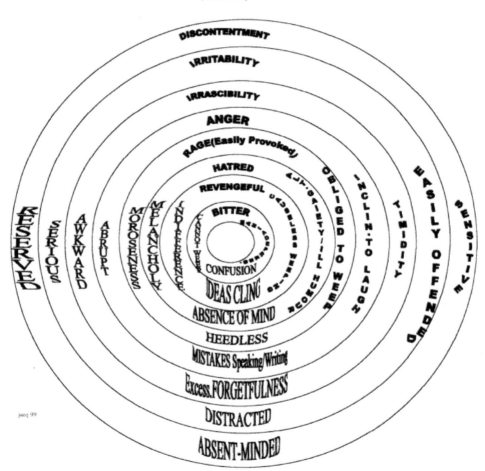

- The symptoms that are most helpful in choosing a remedy are the symptoms which are "**strange, rare and peculiar**", meaning that they are uncommon.
- This is because the strange symptoms are **unique** for the patient and unlike what most other people have.
- **Individualising** the symptoms of a patient is also a principle of respect.
- We respect that no two people are alike, that everyone is special, **unique** and different,
- And that each person needs their own personally matched remedy to get better.
- Once we have gathered all the characteristics of the patient's condition, we look for the remedy that is most similar.

Polychrest Remedies: Rhus Tox commonly known as poison ivy or Rhus Toxicendron, is an upright shrub that can grow to 1 metre tall. Its leaves are 15 centimetres long, alternate, with three leaflets on each. **Latin name:** Toxicodendron pubescens **Family:** Anacardiaceae

FIRE (*HOT/ACTIVE*)

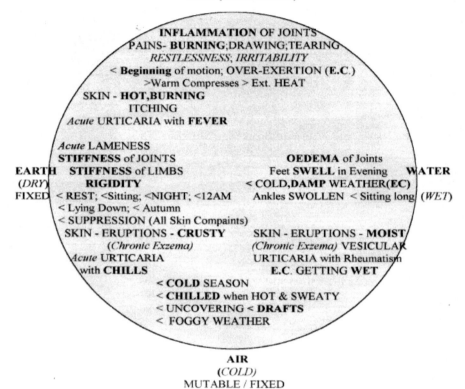

Within the circle:

INFLAMMATION OF JOINTS
PAINS- **BURNING**;DRAWING;TEARING
RESTLESSNESS; IRRITABILITY
< **Beginning** of motion; OVER-EXERTION (**E.C.**)
>Warm Compresses > Ext. HEAT
SKIN - **HOT,BURNING**
ITCHING
Acute URTICARIA with **FEVER**

Acute LAMENESS
STIFFNESS of JOINTS   **OEDEMA** of Joints
EARTH   **STIFFNESS** of LIMBS   Feet **SWELL** in Evening   **WATER**
(*DRY*)   **RIGIDITY**   < **COLD,DAMP** WEATHER(EC)
FIXED   < REST; <Sitting; <NIGHT; <12AM   Ankles SWOLLEN < Sitting long   (*WET*)
< Lying Down; < Autumn
< SUPPRESSION (All Skin Compaints)
SKIN - ERUPTIONS - **CRUSTY**   SKIN - ERUPTIONS - **MOIST**
(*Chronic Exzema*)   (*Chronic Exzema*) VESICULAR
Acute URTICARIA   URTICARIA with Rheumatism
with **CHILLS**   **E.C. GETTING WET**
< **COLD** SEASON
< **CHILLED** when HOT & SWEATY
< **UNCOVERING** < **DRAFTS**
< **FOGGY WEATHER**

AIR
(*COLD*)
MUTABLE / FIXED

RhusTox. is a remedy used in *acute* sprains acting thoroughly to heal connective tissue (after *Arnica*). There is stiffness and trembling with the pain which is tearing or drawing on first movement after rest, but is often better for continued movement. The **Exciting Causes** in this case are often falling, twisting or lifting, which can also produce strain in the joints ie. Over-exertion. Its' relation to **NAT.MUR.** at the *acute* level is the shared affinity of both remedies with connective tissue. The **NAT.MUR.** patient can suffer from *chronic*, <u>old</u> sprains.

Rhus.Tox. – Acute of Chronic – NAT.MUR. cont…..

The patient requiring **Rhus.Tox.** at the first level of inflammation ie. general fevers; can produce Urticaria with chills (**NAT.MUR.** alternating fever and chill). If these eruptions are suppressed by topical application or eg. Anti-histamines they may become *episodic acutes* of eczema which in **Rhus.Tox.** is characteristically expressed in Autumn and is red, sore and inflammed with intense itching. The sores will weep fluid and will then crust over or become dry and raw (**NAT.MUR.** *essence* of Exchange and Polarity). In the *acute episode* it often appears at the hairline, (clustered along nerve tracts (Shingles) is a miasmatic indication); or may be found in the flexures or about the knuckles of the **NAT.MUR.** patient requiring **Rhus.Tox.** At this level, it may be **excited** by the patient getting wet.

The disease process may deepen further due to maintaining causes such as continual exposure to dampness, drafts or over-exertion and further suppression of skin ailments which can result in a shift of symptoms to a local inflammation (*Acute of Chronic*) eg.' Bursitis' (inflammation of the knee joint with hot, painful swelling.)When **Rhus Tox.** is indicated; the symptoms will be better (>) for warm compresses locally and generally external heat and worse (<) for drafts and exertion.

Chronic rheumatism affecting the skeletal system, particularly limbs and joints may be helped if **Rhus Tox.** is the best indicated remedy (See Diagram 6).

Both remedies (ie. **Rhus T. & NAT.MUR.**) share much stiffness and restlessness, the patient unable to keep the legs (especially) still. There may be over-function of fluids here too with the swelling of the feet at night. Particularly indicative of **Rhus Tox.** is the swelling of the ankles after sitting too long. If the patients' limbs and joints in general are worse at rest or when lying down causing the patient to get relief by continual movement eg. Walking around which tires them out or having to change position constantly, then **Rhus Tox.** is the best remedy to deal with this symptom picture.

This rheumatism is much worse in cold, damp (**NAT.MUR.**), wet or foggy (**Rhus Tox.**) weather. They are often worse at night and when **Rhus Tox.** is called for, especially after midnight. Characteristic in this *chronic* state, the patient is often very irritable and just want to be left alone. They are extremely sensitive to cold air (drafts) and therefore worse for uncovering parts of the body. They may also become depressed.

The attempt at giving well-indicated remedies like **Rhus Tox.** at different levels when appropriate would be to try to move the expression of symptoms back up through the levels of disease and out to the skin to prevent increasing rigidity. (The Urticaria can resurface along with rheumatism in the chronic state.)

Polychrest Remedies: Sepia

Sepia is derived from the ink given off by cuttlefish.

NATRUM MURIATICUM – Sepia – *CHRONIC REMEDY*
Diagram 7 – (*Essence – SAG*)

FIRE – HOT
ACTIVE

IRRITABILITY
> OCCUPATION
>> **Violent Exercise / Activity**
Averse Coition & < Coition
Flushes of **Heat** Upwards
>Fast Walking; Dancing

Introspective; Brooding   Vulnerable
'HARDNESS'   < During & After MENSES
FIXED ATTITUDES   < SUPPRESSION of EMOTIONS
EARTH INDIFFERENCE(Esp.Family)   *TEARFUL; WEEPY* **WATER**
DRY   **'SAG'** < *Touch*   < LEFT SIDE   WET
FIXED   << *STANDING*   *EASILY OFFENDED* **MUTABLE**
< **Night;Rest;Sitting**   < *Hormonal Changes*
< Milk;Fats;Acids;Bread*(in pregnancy)   <**Consolation**
Constipation **saif** ball or weight in anus
MATTER OF FACT – DIRECTNESS
Difficult Flow of Ideas
Averse Company
Concentration Difficult when Spoken to
<COLD Weather & Temperature
>SLEEP (even Naps

AIR
COLD
FIXED & MUTABLE

Sepia becomes a *chronic* remedy for the **NAT.MUR.** patient, when the mental state of *Indifference* or apathy has become prominent in their way of dealing with family members. The patient requiring **NAT.MUR.** has many mental and emotional symptoms, but the ensuing *indifference* is a deep state in their disease process. It is evident as being at the fixed pole of the **NAT.MUR.'s** bi-polar nature when there is little or no exchange. The *Vital Force* has become lacking in response other than a concomitant *irritability* characteristic of **Sepia** and which runs through the general symptom picture of **NAT.MUR.**

The *melancholic* (see *The Four Temperaments)* base to the **NAT.MUR.** patients' character supplies them with a deep memory which in the child is poor at first, needing drawn out slowly. They seem to observe the world and in keeping with their bi-polar nature may think themselves unique and therefore cultivate a sense of separateness. They are often serious adults and children, who are shy and introverted (**Sepia**), and may give an impression of heaviness. As children they are often well - behaved, responsible, obedient and ultra co-operative, in order to avoid rejection by parents. The child is very sensitive to disapproval therefore afraid they will not please. If successful in this early precursor to a manipulative trait, we see the tense smile break into a wonderful grin, which transforms their often, pale face, the skin appearing thin.

When their sympathies are aroused, the **NAT.MUR.** child's sensitivity becomes gentleness and kindness. They are easily able to respond to hurt or sick animals. Making friends their own age will take longer due to their lack of confidence and they are often 'loners'. They take impressions deep into the soul, which manifests in the physical body as stomach or head aches. The headaches can be **excited** by the heat of the sun or more fundamentally by emotional shocks such as grief, fright or disappointment. The growing child may worry much, especially at bedtime and can be prone to recurrent nightmares.

They are apt to blame themselves for others' actions resulting in guilt and are wont to punish themselves.

The child may collapse hysterically on hearing of e.g. parental divorce, weeping with an inability to say why. *Ignatia* (see *Diagram 3*) may be better indicated in such an instance to deal with the acute grief.

The growing child or youth finds it difficult to say 'sorry' or to admit mistakes; and as they grow older this becomes a pattern of withdrawal and defence in the form of emotional barriers or in a tendency to arguments and quarrels with the fixed idea that they are 'right' (**Sepia**). These emotional barriers can intensify their feeling of isolation. Their sensitivity predisposes them to easy offence (**Sepia**) and vulnerable to any criticism, deserved or not. Again revealing their bi-polar and exchanging essence is the easy conviction that perceived insults and injuries, no matter how small are meant to hurt.

They neither forget, nor forgive. These grievances will be carried with them into adulthood, as will grief of a deeper nature e.g. deaths; including those of favoured pets. The emotional barrier can result in a 'don't touch me' attitude, often projected onto family, especially parents; compounding their feelings of unworthiness.

The formerly affectionate and well-behaved child can become moody and unhappy, consequently pushing away what they crave most; love and security. The abruptness and irritability (**Sepia**) can manifest here even though the young adolescent will try to control it. They may become prone to alternating diarrhoea and constipation (*see Diagram 2*) in their efforts at retention of anger and loss of control (*Exchange*).

Colic may be concommitant with these symptoms, indicative of their worrying, fearful natures and over time this may deepen into a *chronic* state or appear as an *acute of the chronic* picture of 'Ilietis'.

At this point, as the patient requiring **NAT.MUR.** moves into adulthood proper, the area of relationships involving intimacy and sexual relations becomes more of a focus. Their difficulty in coping with and sustaining relationships becomes more noticeable. Their sympathetic and receptive nature makes them good listeners with insight from a distance, able to offer advice and support to friends, but their own vulnerability is hidden behind a 'hard' façade (**Sepia**) which holds and represses their own deep emotions. They are unable to trust others and may become suspicious of their motives.

The patient may have an ability to manipulate and rationalise their feelings to avoid acknowledging and exposing deep hurts that they may have become quite attached to. They will often experience states of melancholy accompanied by an ensuing *chronic* constipation occurring every second day or at this stage, being prolonged over greater lengths of time.

An increasing feeling of rejection may be felt. This is due both to their inability to open up and share themselves aswell as to the fact that because of the vibration they are projecting to others of suspicion, mistrust etc. they will be left alone. It is possible that after discords the patient when feeling angry will retain fixed ideas, which cling and prevent sleep, sometimes producing feelings of revenge. Though due to an enduring degree of sensitivity and unwillingness to hurt others, they will be blunt and possess a sharp tongue (**Sepia**), but will repress the sharp retort and bottle up their feelings of anger, hurt or ambiguity.

At the physical level, the **NAT.MUR** patient., after spending years holding onto resentments, may produce rheumatic stiffness of limbs and joints (see Diagram 6) and require an *'acute of the chronic'* remedy like **Rhus Tox.** to prevent ensuing *chronic* rigidity.

In a deeply *chronic* state of the Nervous System (e.g. Multiple Sclerosis) further into the disease process, the patient may present with *'Acute'* paralysis
of limbs and dysfunctional proprioception e.g. parts seem too short; numbness on one side; paralysis of fingers. This process manifesting at much deeper levels, better resonates with *Alumina* as the appropriate *chronic* remedy (i.e. *chronic* to **Sepia** and **NAT.MUR.** See Appendix A.)

At these deep emotional levels of dysfunction, the sense of rejection, loneliness and cynicism reaches a place where the patient has become unable to respond in a caring manner and a *chronic* state of *indifference* is produced (*see Diagrams 5 &7.*) The patient no longer cares enough to try to love. They are no longer connected to the feelings of empathy and understanding that they shared with
their family. The responsibility of loving has become a burden (**Sepia).** The partner or children are treated with cold indifference; sagging apathy the result(**Sepia**). Their emotions are hidden behind a smokescreen which obscures their previous sensitivity(**Sepia**). The patient is still generally worse at night but the modality of being better for occupation has shifted to a further pole and has become much better for *violent* exercise or activity(**Sepia**). The mental faculties are sagging and becoming disturbed with difficult flow of ideas, the patient feeling stupid (**Sepia**). The intelligent, attentive thinker who produced considerate and often excellent conversation is losing the ability to sustain concentration and can no longer rely on the source of stimulation that came from within. Physical activity takes this place as a way of activating the vitality (*Exchange & Polarity*). The patient may now weep for no cause but are still worse for any consolation(**Sepia**).

They will feel worse for having to remain in any 'fixed' position, especially standing, which can aggravate a 'bearing down' sensation in the uterus; the burden they carry around inside ?

This is often verbalised in those needing **Sepia** by the expression ' I can't stand it/this' or they complain that they feel as if they carry a weight around on their back.

Sepia as a well - chosen *chronic* remedy here, would hope to begin shifting the symptom picture to allow for more flexibility and less weight of negativity on the mental and emotional levels. This may help the patient alter their perception of life to one that is less heavily burdened. It would help give the patients' *Vital Force* the much needed boost to lift the symptoms from a *chronic* mental and emotional state, further up the disease process towards possibly less disabling physical symptoms.

References/Credits

Pg. 14 Image credits: Alex Grey. The Mission of Art, Shambhala Ltd, 1998

Pg. 16 Symphony No. 1; previously published on Hpathy.com, 20th June 2014

Pg. 23 & 24 Law of Cure images Sarah Walder

Pg. 33 Between Form and Freedom, Betty K, Staley, Hawthorn Press, 1988

Pg. 46 Salt image adobe free stock image

Pg. 66 Four Elements image adobe free stock image

Pg. 69 Bryonia image adobe free stock image

Pg. 58/68 Emotional Anatomy, The Structure of Experience, Stanley Kelleman, Centre Press, 1984

Pg. 70 Rhus Tox image adobe free stock image

Pg. 74 Sepia image adobe free stock image

Organon of the Rational Art of Medicine-S. Hahnemann

Atom free stock image

Cover image: Dreamstime.com

All other images/infographics/tables: ©Jacqueline Smith

Acknowledgements

Thanks to all the great homeopaths down the ages and the inspiring contemporary advancements in our Art & Science. To my colleagues in the Ghana Homeopathy Project and especially to all the patients and family encountered here and there who brought Hahnemann's philosophy to life with their incredibly dynamic responses to treatment, so much so that they dubbed it 'magic'; a very Glaswegian sentiment.

About the Author

Jacqueline has been a homeopathic practitioner for twenty-five years after graduating with Distinction from The Scottish College of Homeopathy in 1997. She studied with Prof George Vithoulkas in Greece in 1999 & 2004, at The Bengal Allen Medical Institute, India, 2007 and was Coordinator for the Ghana Homeopathy Project 2014-17 where she travelled to Ghana, living and working there for several months each year. She is now a trustee.

Jacqueline graduated from the Creative Writing MLitt. at Glasgow University in 2012. In 2010 she also ran Poetry@The Ivory and in 2013, Pothole Press published *'Inspiration from the Common Wealth of Writers to Boost Creativity'* based on Ivory author interviews as an e-book. In 2015 it was then published in print by Fleming Publications. Jacqueline is also a former Chair of the Scottish Writers Centre, *'The Scottish Witchfinder'* was published by Fleming Publications in 2018. The first novel she wrote, *'The Two Seeings'* was also published in print and e-book editions in 2018 with the Independent Publishing Network, as was *Slaves of Men and Gods*, set in Ghana (2020), and two poetry Collections, *Fragility* and *Mosaic* in 2021

She has before and since had several articles published in various health and well-being mag and e-zines, including www.Hpathy.com and previous monthly contributions to www.SibylMagazine.com - *For the Spirit and Soul of Woman*. 2018

Catch up with Jacqueline at:

Website: www.wordsmithjacqueline.com

https://www.facebook.com/wordsmithjacq/
https://twitter.com/CreativeLifeJac

Other books by Jacqueline A. Smith

ICWW & SWF Print: www.flemingpublications.com
ICWW Ebook ISBN: ISBN 978-1-910033-03-6
TS Print- ISBN: 978-1-78926-230-8
TS E-book- ISBN: 978-1-78926-723-5
https://www.amazon.co.uk/-/e/B00HLSMYKS